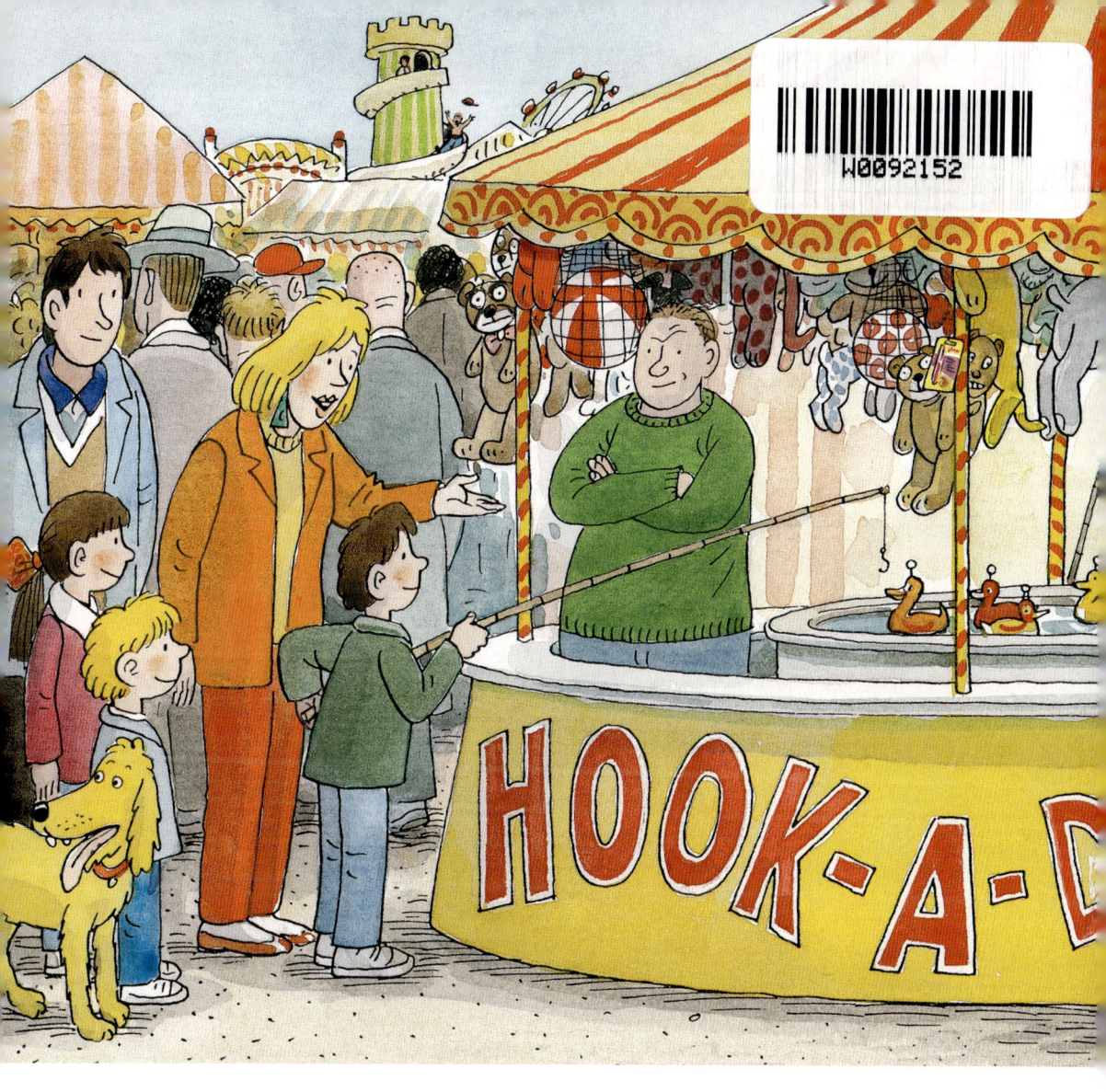

"Hook a duck," said Mum.

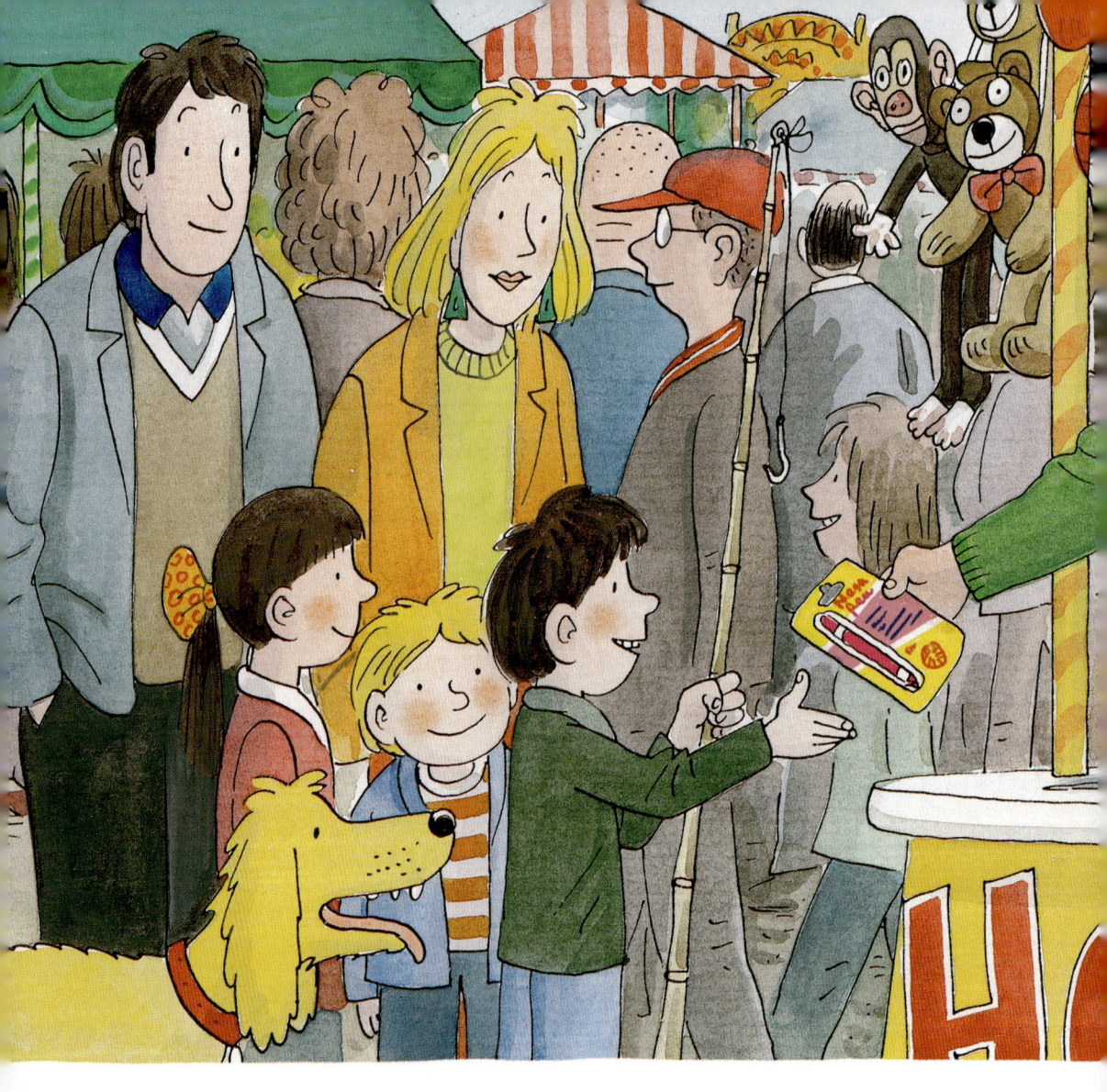

Chip had a go.

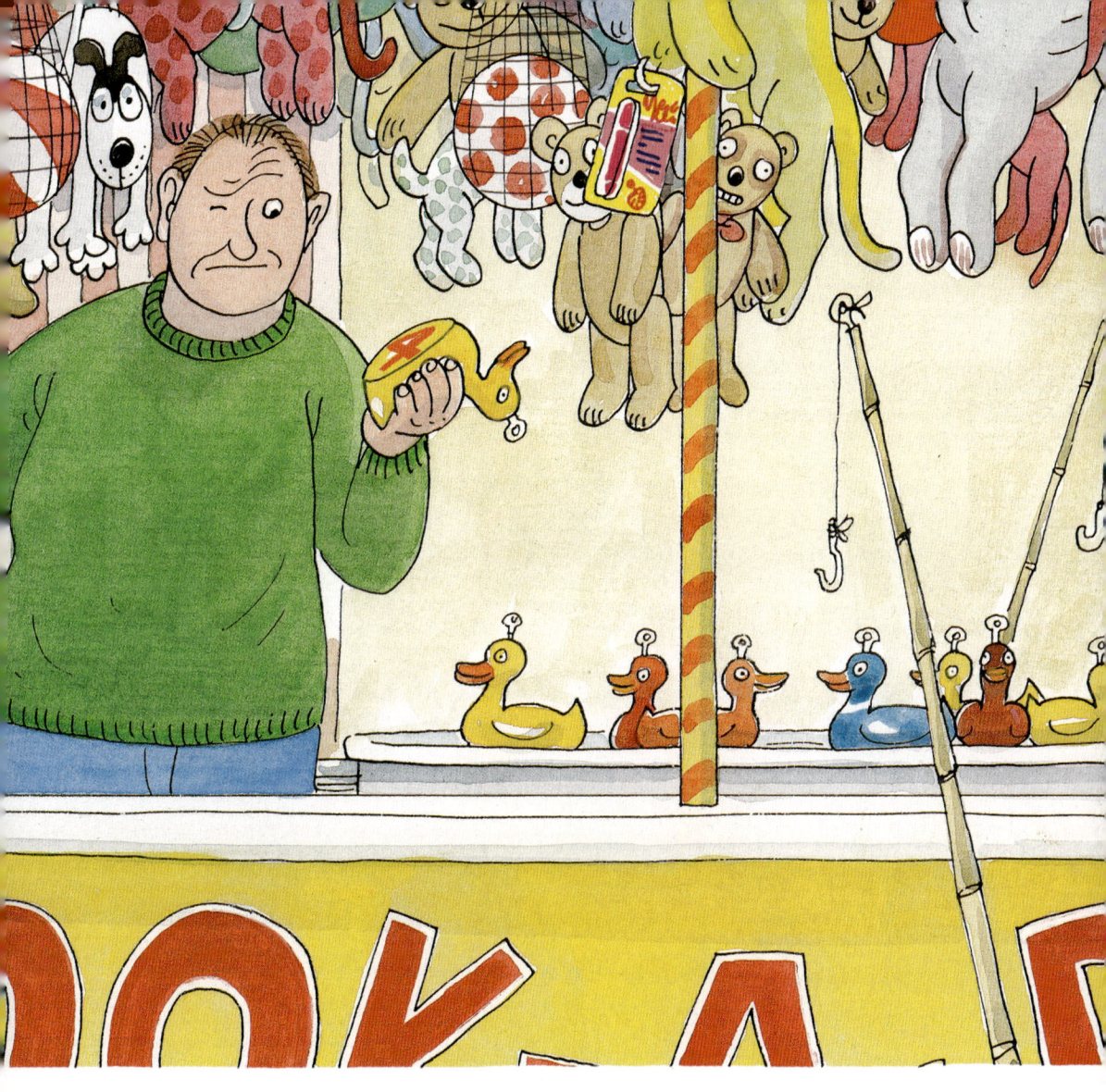

He got a pen.

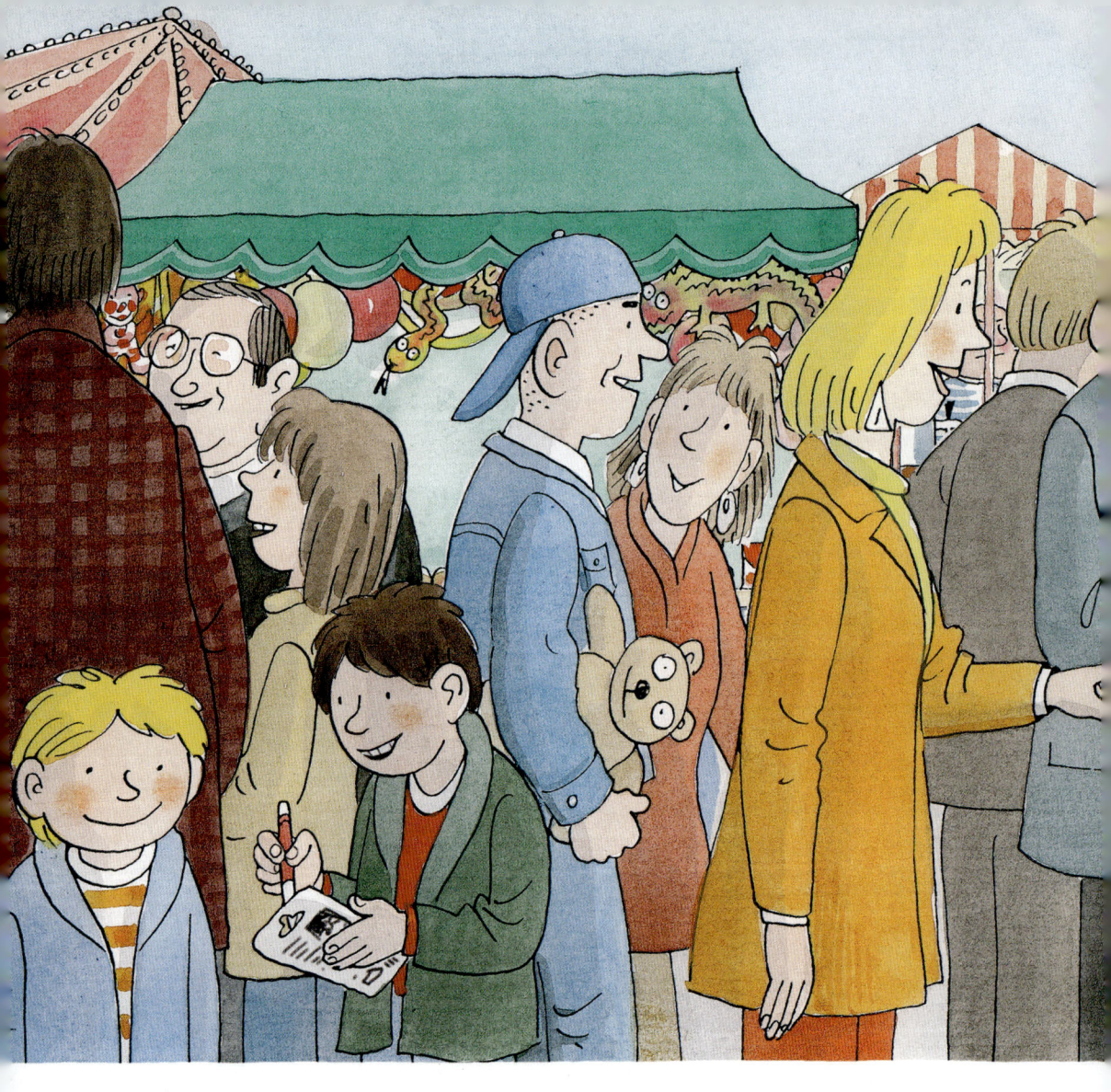

"Have a go," said Mum.

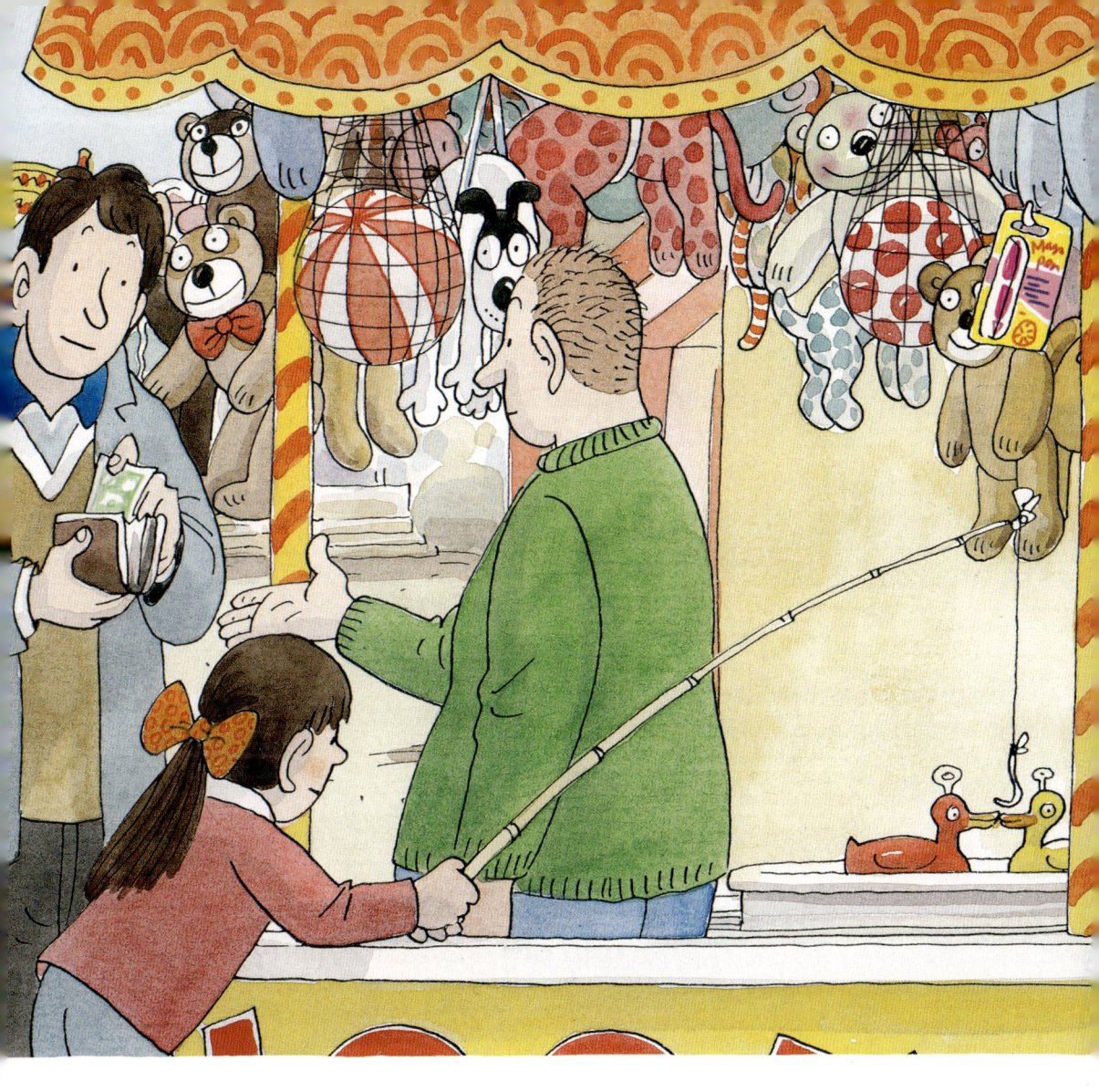

Biff had a go.

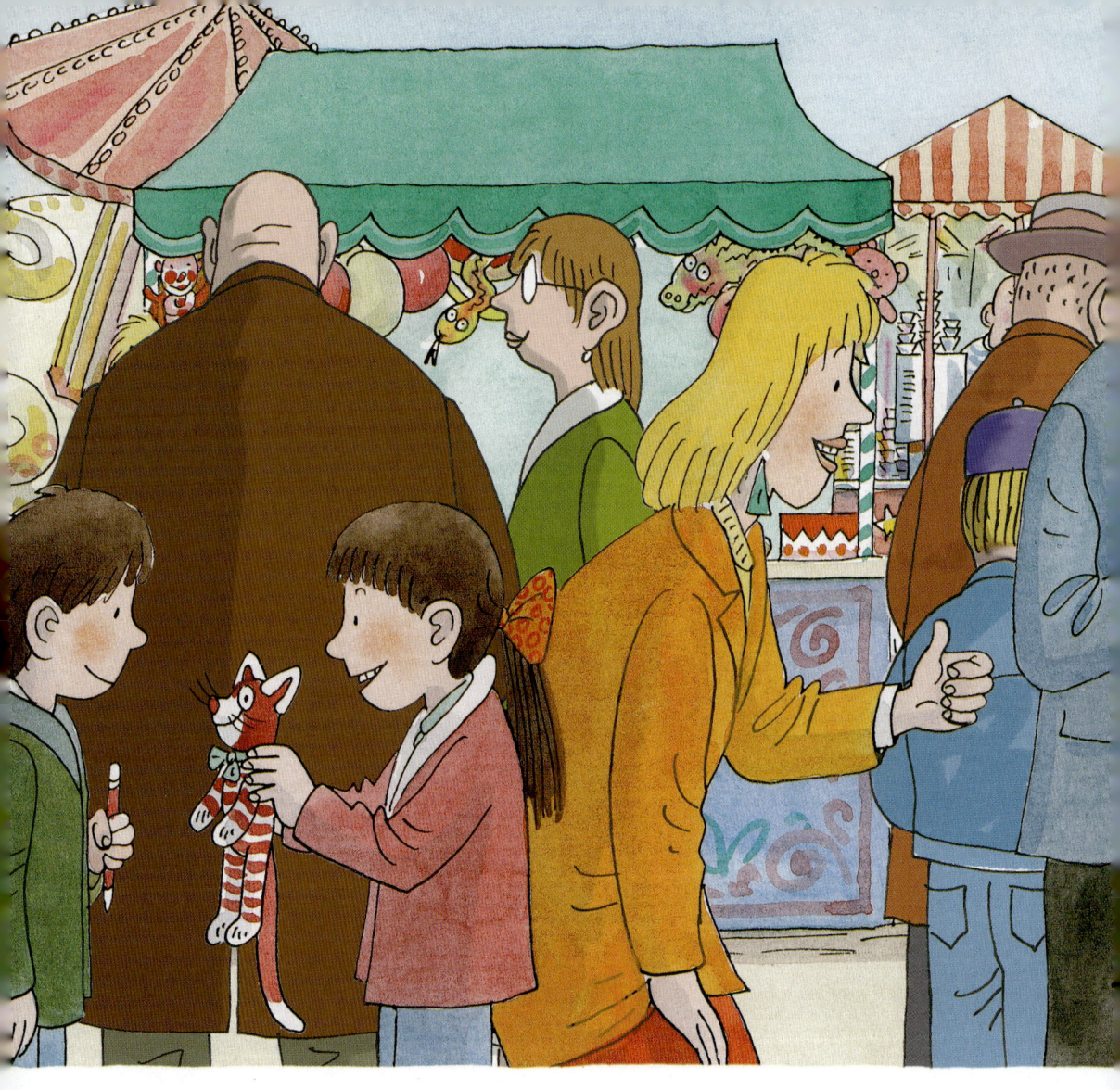

Biff got a cat.

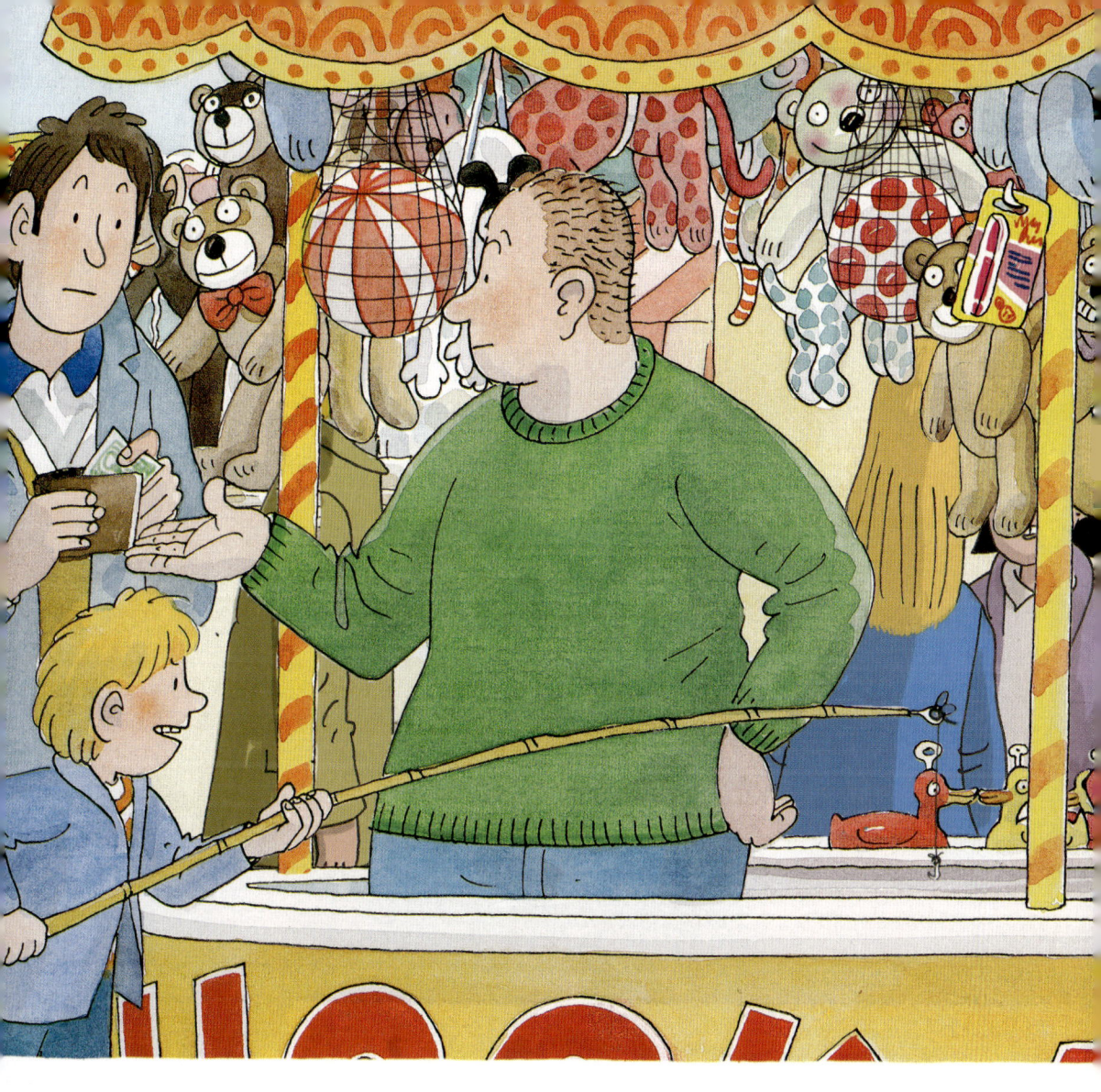

"Go on. Hook a duck," said Mum.

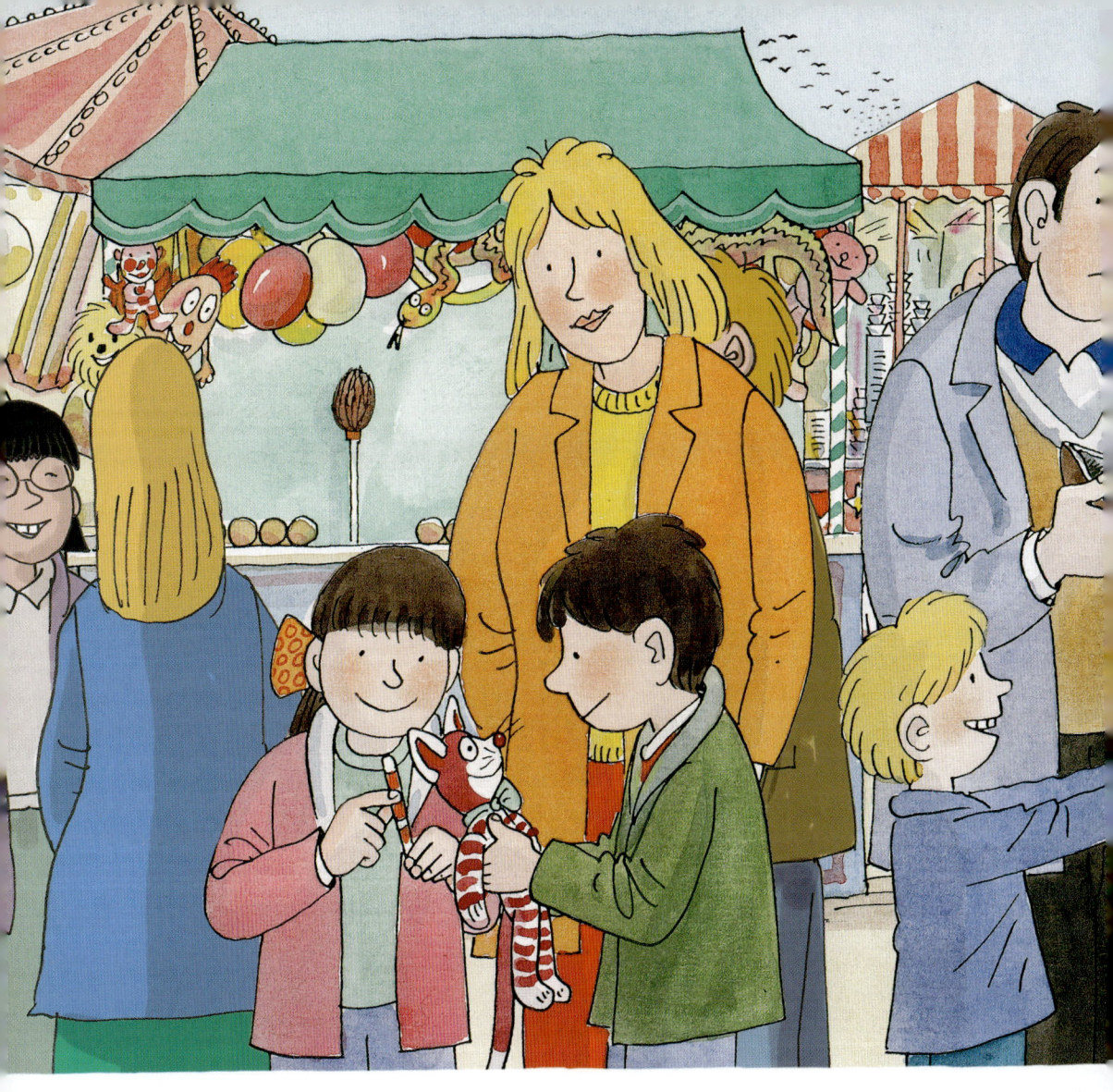

Kipper had a go.

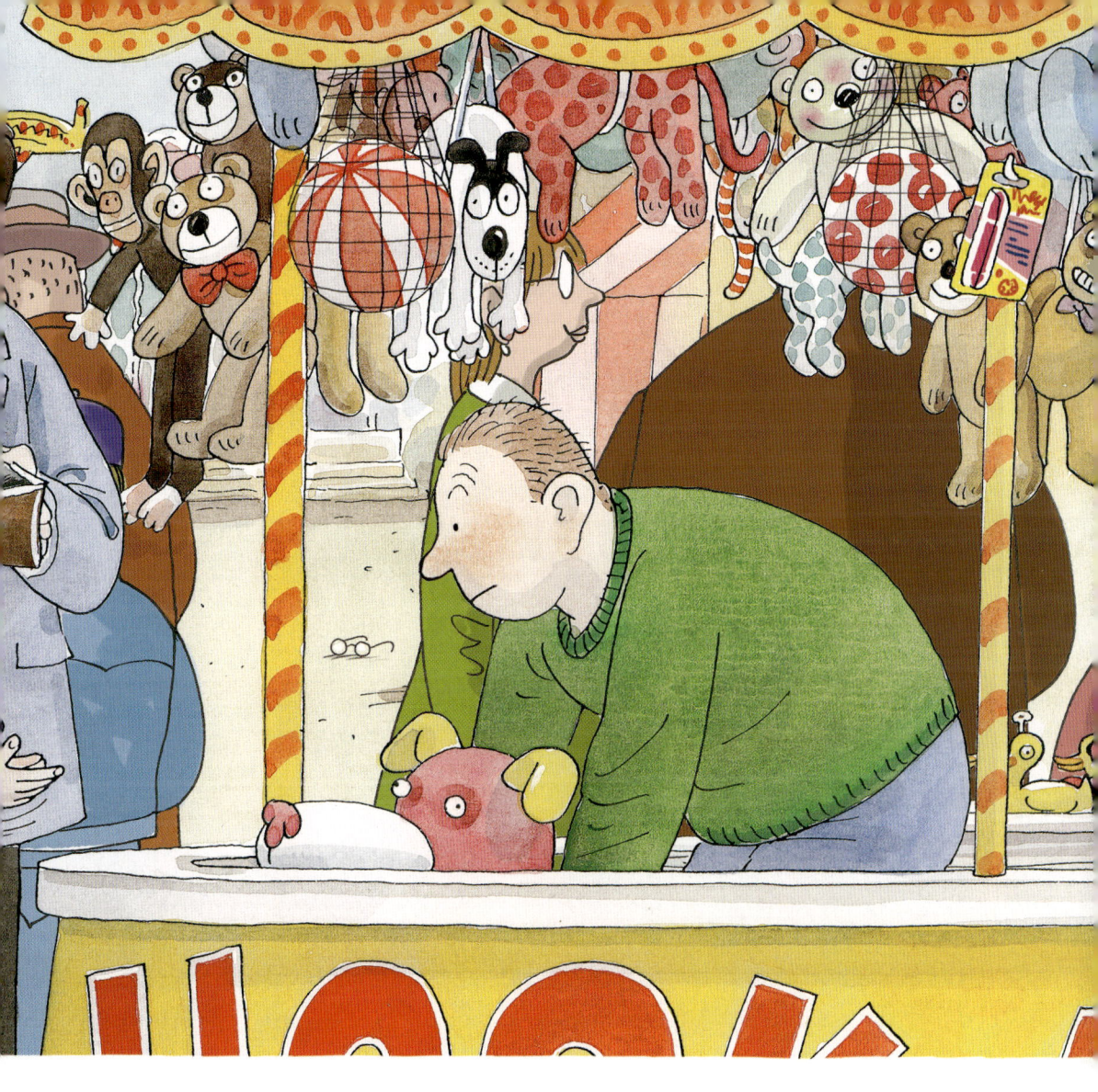

He got a dog.

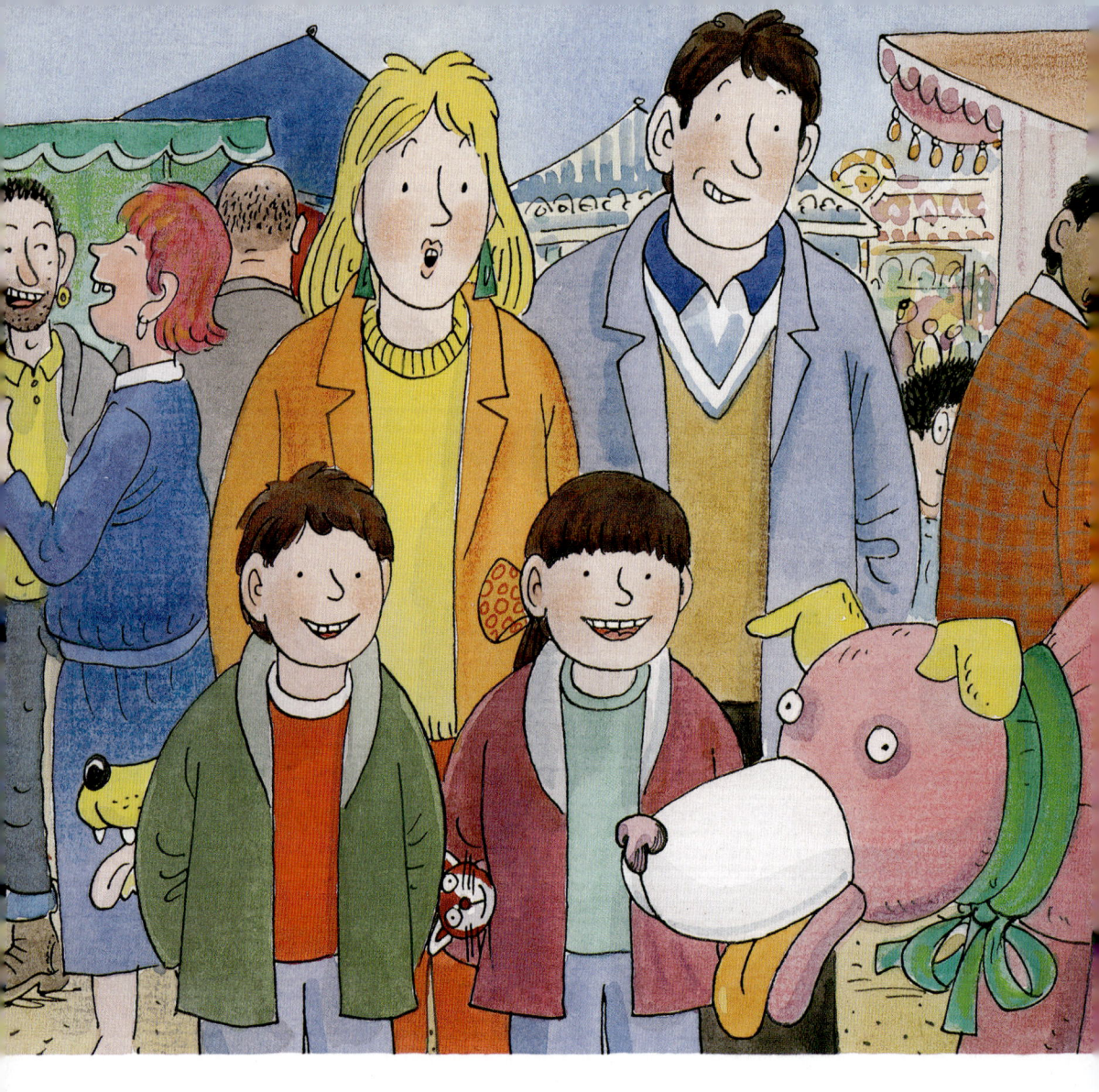

It was a big dog.

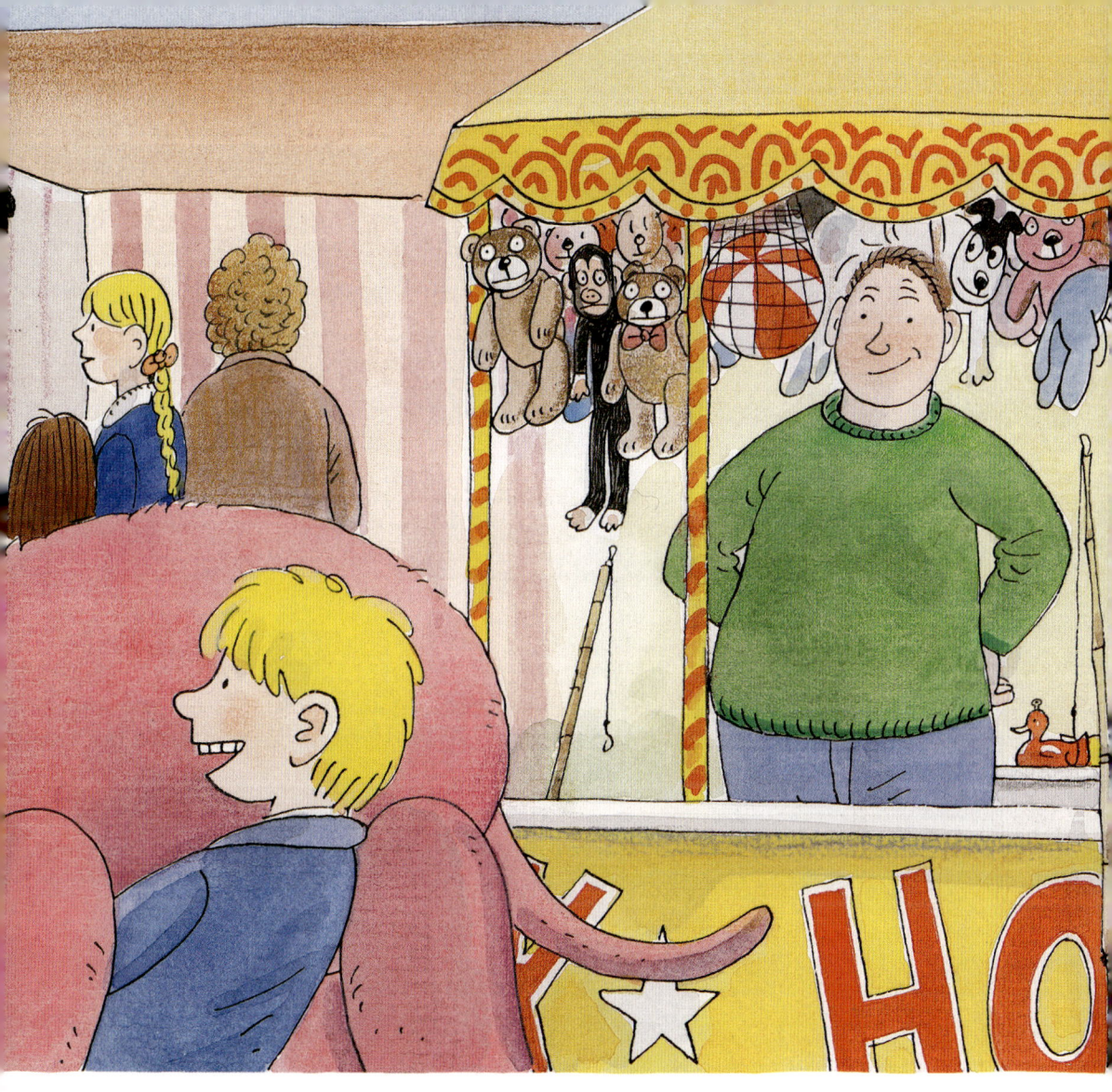

"What a big dog!" said Kipper.

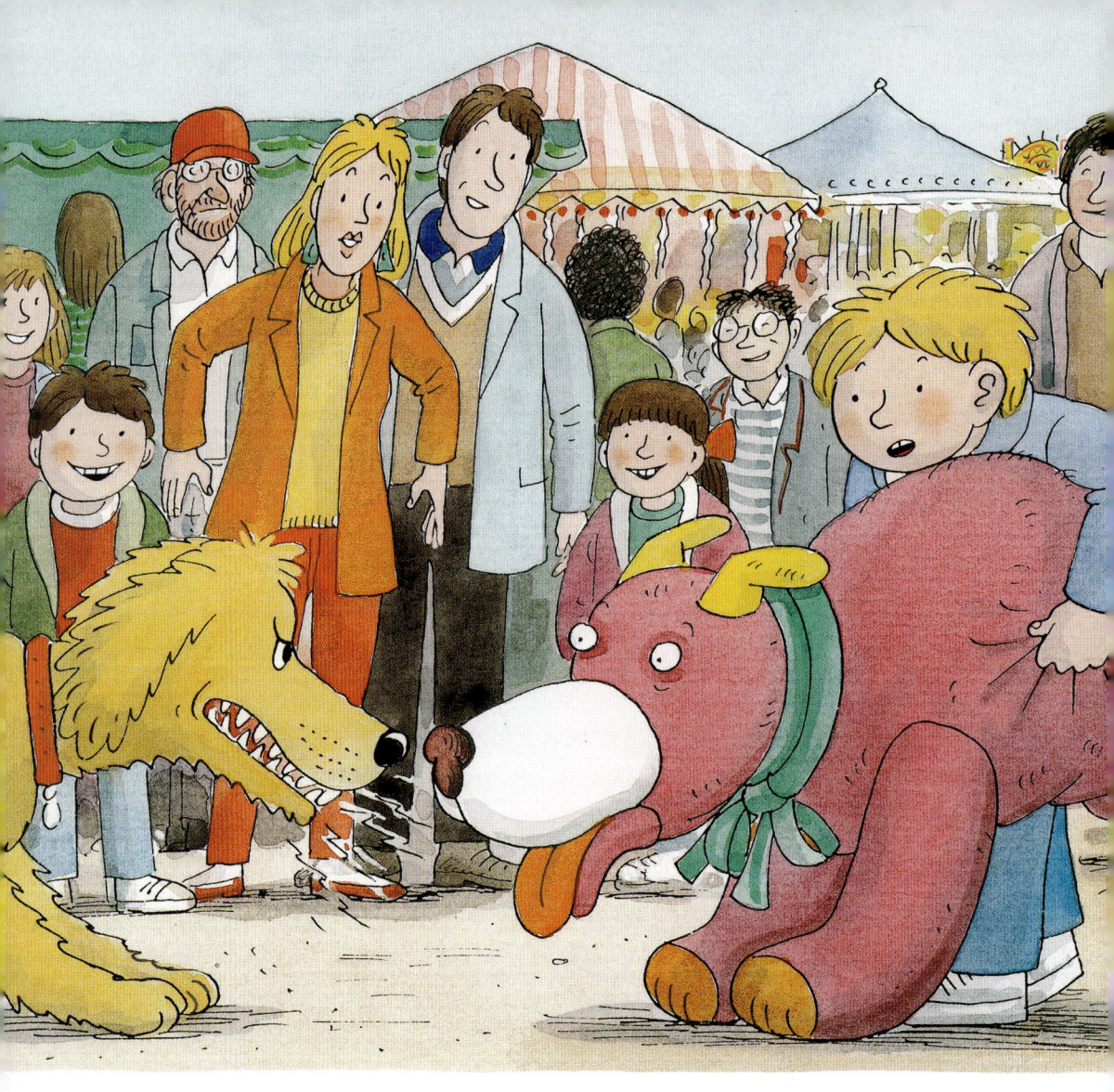

"Grrr!" said Floppy.